Series 522

The Child of the Temple

told by LUCY DIAMOND

illustrated by
KENNETH INNS

Publishers: Wills & Hepworth Ltd., Loughborough

THE CHILD OF THE TEMPLE

Long long ago in the land of Israel, a man named Elkanah and Hannah his wife lived at Ramah, a little village among the hills.

Their house was built high up on the hillside. All around it were olive groves and vineyards, where at harvest time the ripened grapes hung in large purple bunches from the pretty green vines.

It was a beautiful house with a lovely garden.

Elkanah loved his wife dearly and did everything he could to make her happy.

Yet Hannah was sad! Sometimes she sat and cried for hours and refused to eat. Her beautiful rooms were lonely and too quiet. She had no children—no little boys and girls to play there, or run about in the sunny garden. There were children in another part of the house, but they were not Hannah's—and when she heard their happy voices calling to each other, and laughing at their play, she felt sadder than ever.

"Why do you fret so?" Elkanah asked. "Am I not better to you than ten sons when I love you so dearly!"

But Hannah would not be comforted.

"If only I had one little boy," she kept on saying. "If only I had a small son, I should have nothing left to wish for!"

Now Elkanah and all his household worshipped the one true God—the God of Israel. They called him the Lord Jehovah.

At that time the temple of the Lord was in Shiloh, and Eli the priest and his two sons were there. Shiloh was about fifteen miles from Ramah, but once every year Elkanah went from his own city to worship and to sacrifice to the Lord of Hosts in Shiloh.

Hannah and all his household went with him on his journey, and took with them offerings of corn, and wine, and oil, and the best of all they had, to give to the Lord Jehovah—just as we take our offerings to God's house at harvest time.

One year, when they all started out, Hannah felt sadder than ever as she saw young boys of Elkanah's household going happily along in the procession, carrying their offerings to the Lord Jehovah.

After the journey they all sat down to eat their supper before they rested for the night in Shiloh, ready for the service of worship and sacrifices the next morning.

But Hannah could not eat! She stole away from the rest of the company, and went alone to the temple of the Lord. She was so miserable and unhappy that she wanted to tell God all about it, and ask Him to help her.

So she stood within the entrance to the temple weeping and praying!

"O Lord of Hosts," she prayed, "Look upon me and help me in my trouble. Give me a little son! If only you will give me a little boy of my own, I will give him back to you, to serve the Lord Jehovah all the days of his life."

Hannah stood weeping and praying before the Lord — but she prayed in her heart and, though her lips moved, no sound came from them.

Eli the priest was sitting by the door of the temple, and saw Hannah come and stand there all alone. She looked wild and distracted as if she did not know what she was doing. "How strangely that woman is behaving," he thought.

At last he got up and went to her.

"Do you know what you are doing?" he said sternly. "You must not behave like this in the temple of the Lord!"

"Oh, sir," said poor Hannah, "I am only praying! I am dreadfully unhappy and miserable. I felt I must tell the Lord about it, and beg of Him to help me. Indeed I did not mean to be wicked or careless in the temple of the Lord."

She did not tell the old priest why she had been praying so earnestly, but when Eli looked into her sorrowful face, and heard what she said, he was no longer angry. He spoke kindly to her.

"Go in peace," he said. "May the God of Israel comfort you, and give you what you have prayed for."

So Hannah went happily away! Now she could eat, and her face was no longer sad. She got up early in the morning, and joined with the others in the temple service. Then they all went back to Ramah.

God did give Hannah what she had prayed for! By and by she had a little son, and she called his name Samuel—which means "heard of God."

"Because," she said, "I have asked him of the Lord."

Then how happy Elkanah and his wife were! Baby Samuel was the most precious thing in all that beautiful house—and how tenderly his Mother watched over and cared for him!

But Hannah had promised to give her little child back to God, and she did not forget.

That year when they were all getting ready to go to Shiloh, Hannah said to her husband, "I will not go with you this time. Baby Samuel is too young to be left. I must stay at home to look after him. We must wait until he can run about, and feed himself, and dress himself. Then we will take him to the temple of the Lord."

And Elkanah said, "You must do as you think best—but when our little one is old enough, we must do as you promised, and give him back to God."

So for a time Hannah kept her little son, but he was still only very young when at last she and Elkanah took him to Shiloh.

They carried with them wine and flour, and other offerings for the Lord Jehovah, and so they came to Eli in the temple.

How surprised the old priest was when he saw the tall father and the smiling mother with their beautiful little boy. He did not remember Hannah — for she looked so different from the strange woman to whom he had once spoken!

"Oh, sir," said this happy mother, "I am the woman who stood by you here, and prayed unto the Lord. I prayed for this child—and see, the Lord has given him to me."

"Now I give him back to God. He shall stay here with you, to serve the Lord Jehovah in His temple, as long as he lives."

Eli the priest smiled at the little child who looked up at him with big shining eyes, wondering what was going to happen. Eli put his kind arms around Samuel, and drew him close to his side.

"You shall stay here with me," he said. "I will teach you to serve the Lord Jehovah in His holy temple."

Then Hannah sang a hymn of praise and thanksgiving to God and, after they had made their sacrifice, they said goodbye to their small son, and started back to Ramah.

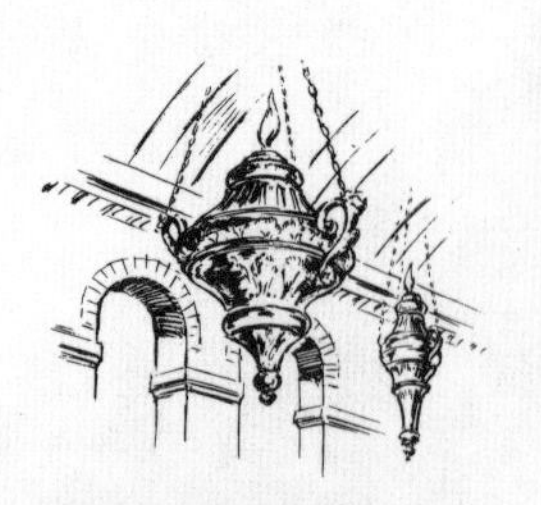

Elkanah and Hannah went home—while Samuel stayed in Shiloh—such a little boy to be left all alone with strangers without his father and mother !

But Eli the priest was kind and gentle, and loved little children. He was so glad to have Hannah's precious son that he took the greatest care of the child, and did all he could to make him happy in his new home.

Eli was a lonely old man. His two sons were supposed to help in the temple—but they were selfish and wicked. They stole the offerings of the people and when their father rebuked them they took no notice. He had spoiled them when they were boys. Now they cared nothing for him.

So Eli rejoiced to have Hannah's little son living with him in the temple. The two became great friends. Eli was old and tired, and he was going blind, so it was a great help to him to have the boy's quick feet and nimble fingers to fetch and carry for him—always so happily and willingly. Now that he was the child of the temple, Samuel wore a little tunic of white linen fastened with a belt. He soon learned how to help with the daily work which kept everything in the house of God in sweet and fresh order, and how to make ready for the services in the temple.

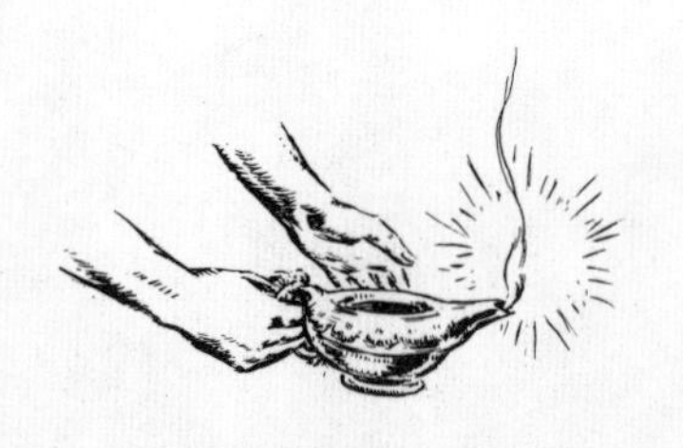

Samuel began to love this house of God in Shiloh. Everything in it was so beautiful. It was full of lovely things fashioned in gold, silver and brass, and enriched in glowing colours by the most skilful artists and craftsmen in Israel—all working with love in their hearts, and giving of their very best for the glory of the Lord Jehovah!

The most wonderful and sacred thing in Shiloh was the Ark of God. This stood in the temple behind the beautiful curtains which shut off the holiest place of all where only the priest of God might go.

The Ark was made of fragrant acacia wood covered with gold. Above its lid was the mercy seat where two golden angels faced each other with wings outspread.

A lamp filled with pure olive oil burned all night before the Ark—a little flame to remind those who saw it, that even through

the dark hours, the Lord Jehovah was watching over His people.

So as the days and months went by, the child Samuel was happy in his life in the temple.

Each year when Hannah came up to Shiloh, she brought Samuel a little coat she had made for him to wear over his tunic. We may think how glad and proud Hannah would be, as she fitted this on to her son, and saw how he had grown! The next year she would have to make a still bigger coat!

Hannah was a happy woman now. She and Elkanah had other children, three sons

and two daughters—brothers and sisters of Samuel. Perhaps sometimes her eldest son went back to visit the house at Ramah—but his real home now was the temple of the Lord in Shiloh, where he and Eli the priest lived their quiet days together.

Then something very strange and very wonderful happened !

One night when the services of the day were over, and the evening hymn had been sung, Eli was laid down to rest in his place in the temple. Samuel was fast asleep, curled up on his little mattress close by where the Ark of God was.

All was very quiet, very still in the temple of the Lord !

Yet something woke Samuel !

He sat up and looked around. What had roused him? It was not yet morning, for the lamp which burned before the Ark of God from evening until sunrise had not gone out. Its flame still threw a dim golden light across the shadows of the dark temple.

Then a voice came clearly through the stillness.

"Samuel!"

It must be Eli, the boy thought.

"I'm coming," he called, as he jumped up and ran to where the old priest slept.

“ Here I am,” he said. “ You called me.”

Eli was surprised. “ I didn’t call you, my child, he said. “ Go and lie down again.”

So Samuel went back and lay down.

But before he dropped off to sleep, once more the voice came.

“ Samuel ! ”

Again the boy jumped up, and ran to Eli, saying, “ Here I am, for you did call me ! ”

“ No, my son,” the old priest answered, “ I didn’t call you. Perhaps you were dreaming. Go and lie down again.”

So the boy went slowly back to his mattress and lay down. He was puzzled, because he felt certain he had heard someone call.

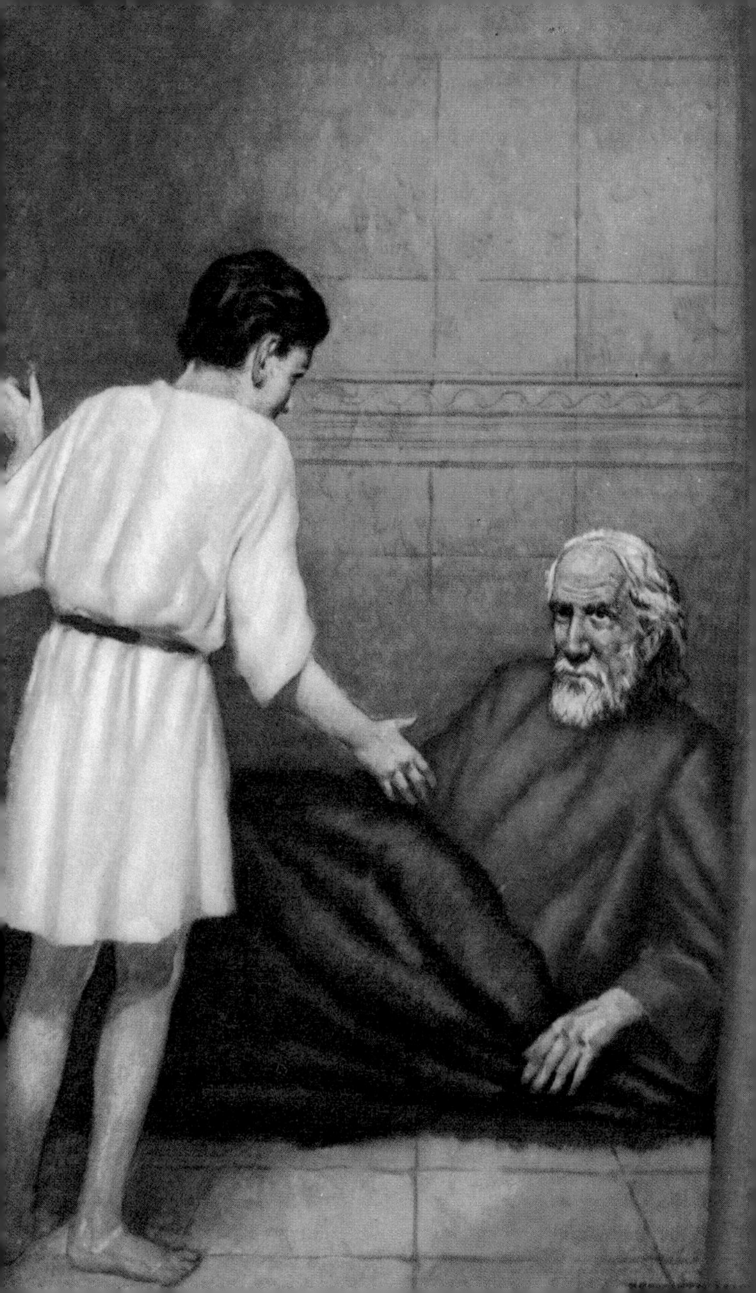

Hardly had he settled down to try to sleep, when again the voice came. Clearly and distinctly ringing through the silent temple, he heard his name !

" Samuel ! Samuel ! "

Once more the boy ran as quickly as he could to Eli.

" Here I am," he said. " I know you called me this time. I heard you. I wasn't dreaming ! "

Then the old priest knew that the Lord had called the child. Samuel had never

heard God's voice before and had not known it.

Quietly, Eli put out his frail old hands and drew this dearly loved child close to him.

" Listen, my son," he said gently. " Go and lie down, and if you hear the call again, say, " Speak, Lord, for your servant hears."

So Samuel went and lay down in his place, and listened and listened, wondering if the voice would come again.

Then the Lord came and called as he had done before—" Samuel ! Samuel ! "

And little Samuel whispered, " Speak, for your servant hears."

Then God spoke to Samuel, and in the stillness of the night the boy heard every word.

They were very sad words !

"I have seen how wicked the sons of Eli are and they shall never take his place as priests of the Lord in Shiloh."

So the Lord spoke to Samuel and told him what he meant to do in Israel. By the time the voice was hushed, the boy knew that he was the one chosen to take Eli's place and one day would be the priest of God.

He did not sleep again but lay thinking until the lamp before the Ark went out and the faint light of dawn showed that the night had gone.

Then he got up and opened the doors of the temple, letting in the morning sunshine.

But he did not go at once to Eli! He was troubled. He loved the kind old priest, and did not wish to cause him sorrow!

So he was afraid to tell Eli what the Lord had said to him.

But as he moved about, Samuel heard his name called—and this time he knew it was Eli.

"Samuel, my son. Where are you?"

Slowly, the boy went towards the place where Eli lay.

"Here I am," he said, as he stood quietly by.

The blind old priest could not see the boy's face, but he could hear that his voice sounded dull and sad.

"My child," he said. "What is wrong? What did the Lord say to you in the night?"

But Samuel did not speak. He could not bear to tell such a terrible thing to the old man he had come to love so dearly.

"Don't be afraid," Eli went on. "If you would help me, tell me all that the Lord said to you."

So, very sadly, the boy told Eli everything. He hid nothing from him of all that the Lord had spoken.

Sorrowfully the old priest bowed his head.

"It is the Lord," he said. "Let Him do what seems good to Him."

All that day Samuel went so sadly about his work, that Eli knew he was worried and distressed.

The old man tried to comfort the boy who had found God's message so hard to tell.

"God has called you to do great things for Him," he said. "You are worthy, my child! You are faithful and true, and I am glad that you are chosen to take my place when I am gone."

From that day, the tired old priest and the young boy were dearer to each other than ever. Samuel grew, and the Lord was with him, and watched over him.

As the boy went quietly and joyfully about his duties in the temple, he began to understand more and more what the Lord Jehovah was like, and what it meant to serve him truly.

And, as time went on, it was known throughout the land that Samuel, the child of the temple, was chosen to be, when he grew up, the priest of the Lord in Shiloh, and his prophet in Israel.

So, in after years, Samuel became the leader and the judge of God's people Israel. He went back to live in his house at Ramah, and there he built an altar to the Lord.

When at last his long life ended Samuel was buried in Ramah and all Israel came together to do honour to a good and wise man, and a mighty prophet of the Lord.

Series 522